Geronimo Stilton

PAPERCUTZ ™

Geronimo Stilton

GRAPHIC NOVELS AVAILABLE FROM PAPERCUTZ™

Graphic Novel #1
"The Discovery
of America"

Graphic Novel #2
"The Secret
of the Sphinx"

Graphic Novel #3
"The Coliseum Con"

Graphic Novel #4
"Following the Trail
of Marco Polo"

Graphic Novel #5
"The Great Ice Age"

Graphic Novel #6
"Who Stole The
Mona Lisa?"

Graphic Novel #7
"Dinosaurs in Action"

Graphic Novel #8
"Play It Again, Mozart!"

Graphic Novel #9
"The Weird Book
Machine"

Graphic Novel #10
"Geronimo Stilton Saves
the Olympics"

Graphic Novel #11
"We'll Always
Have Paris"

Graphic Novel #12
"The First Samurai"

GERONIMO STILTON graphic novels are available for $9.99 each only in hardcover. Available from booksellers everywhere. You can also order online from www.papercutz.com. Or call 1-800-886-1223, Monday through Fridays, 9 – 5 EST. MC, Visa, and AmEx accepted. To order by mail, please add $4.00 for postage and handling for first book ordered, $1.00 for each additional book and make check payable to NBM Publishing. Send to: Papercutz, 160 Broadway, Suite 700, East Wing, New York, NY 10038. GERONIMO STILTON graphic novels are also available digitally wherever e-books are sold.

www.papercutz.com

Geronimo Stilton

THE FIRST SAMURAI

By Geronimo Stilton

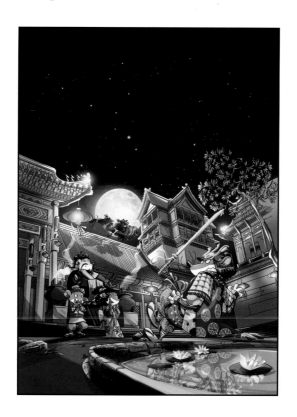

NEW YORK

THE FIRST SAMURAI
© EDIZIONI PIEMME 2011 S.p.A.
Corso Como 15, 20145,
Milan, Italy
Graphics and Illustrations © Atlantyca Entertainment S.p.A. 2011
Geronimo Stilton names, characters and related indicia are copyright, trademark and
exclusive license of Atlantyca S.p.A.
All rights reserved.
The moral right of the author has been asserted.

Text by Geronimo Stilton
Editorial coordination by Patrizia Puricelli
Artistic coordination by BAO Publishing
Story by Michele Foschini
Script by Leonardo Favia
Illustrations by Ennio Bufi and color by Mirka Andolfo
Cover by effeeffestudios
Cover Design by Marta Lorini
Based on an original idea by Elisabetta Dami

© 2013 – for this work in English language by Papercutz.

Original title: "Il Primo Samurai"

Translation by: Nanette McGuinness

www.geronimostilton.com

Lettering and Production by Ortho
Michael Petranek – Associate Editor
Jim Salicrup
Editor-in-Chief

ISBN: 978-1-62991-181-6

Printed in China.
August 2014 by WKT Co. LTD.
3/F Phase 1 Leader Industrial Centre
188 Texaco Road, Tsuen Wan, N.T.
Hong Kong

Distributed by Macmillan
Second Papercutz Printing

OUR ADVENTURE BEGAN AT THE NEW MOUSE CITY **GOURMET** FAIR, WHERE I HAD ARRANGED TO MEET MY COUSIN TRAP.

UNCLE, WE'RE EARLY. IT'S NOT YET NOON. TRAP WON'T HAVE ARRIVED YET.

BY THE WAY, I HAVEN'T INTRODUCED MYSELF YET. MY NAME IS STILTON, *Geronimo Stilton*, AND I EDIT THE RODENT'S GAZETTE, THE MOST FAMOUSE PAPER ON MOUSE ISLAND!

TRAP'S USUALLY NEVER ON TIME. THERE'S NO WAY HE'LL BE EARLY!

-PSSST!-

WHAT--?! WHO ARE YOU?

IT'S ME, GERONIMO! I HAVE TO BE VERY **CAREFUL**...

WHAT'S GOING ON? WHY ARE YOU IN DISGUISE?

AND WHY ARE YOU SO EARLY?

IT'S BECAUSE OF WHAT HAPPENED LAST YEAR, AT THE LAST GOURMET FAIR...

"...LET'S SAY THAT I OVERDID IT A BIT AT A STAND WHERE I WASN'T INVITED..."

"...AND I WAS BANNED FROM EVER ATTENDING THIS EVENT AGAIN."

THEN I **CERTAINLY** WON'T LET YOU IN!

I PROMISE I WON'T MAKE TROUBLE THIS TIME...

TRY TO UNDERSTAND... A FAIR WITH THE BEST CHEFS IN NEW MOUSE CITY... HOW COULD I MISS IT?

REMEMBER TO BEHAVE YOURSELF. YOU GAVE ME YOUR WORD AS A RODENT!

DON'T WORRY, COUSIN. I'LL BE A MODEL VISITOR...

THANK YOU.

THANK YOU.

HMM...

HMM...

~GULP!~

WILL YOU GET A MOVE ON?!

THANK YOU.

INCREDIBLE... I DIDN'T THINK THEY'D STILL REMEMBER ME...

MAYBE THIS TIME YOU'LL BEHAVE, SO YOU WON'T HAVE TO RUN THIS RISK NEXT YEAR!

TRY TO STAY CALM AND DON'T GET YOURSELF NOTICED AS YOU USUALLY DO...

ER-- UNCLE...

?!

BEING CALM ISN'T HIS STRENGTH, ESPECIALLY WITH THE AROMA OF FOOD IN THE AIR!

CHARGE!

IT'S REALLY STRONGER THAN HE IS, HUH?

HE'S THE BIGGEST GLUTTON OF ANY RAT I'VE EVER KNOWN...

I'M CURIOUS TO SEE HOW HE'S GOING CONVINCE THE CHEFS TO LET HIM SAMPLE THEIR SPECIALTIES... BUT NOW I HAVE TO DO A FEW INTERVIEWS.

GOOD AFTERNOON, MY NAME IS STILTON, *Geronimo Stilton*, AND I EDIT THE RODENT'S GAZETTE. I'D LIKE TO ASK YOU A FEW QUESTIONS...

I ALREADY SPOKE WITH YOUR COLLEAGUE AND LET ME TELL YOU, HE BEHAVED VERY BADLY!

HE TOLD ME THAT TO GIVE ME A GOOD REVIEW, HE'D HAVE TO TASTE **EVERYTHING**...

I THOUGHT HE MEANT A LITTLE OF EVERYTHING...

...NOT **EVERYTHING**!

WE'RE RUINED...

WHAT HAPPENED?

HE SAID HE WAS CURIOUS TO TRY OUR LATEST DISHES... THAT HE'D WRITE A FABULOUS REVIEW...

HE ATE EVERYTHING WE'D COOKED. AND WE DON'T HAVE MORE DISHES FOR VISITORS TO THE FAIR.

TRAP...

TRAP HAS GOTTEN CARRIED AWAY. HE'S PROMISING ARTICLES IN EXCHANGE FOR ENORMOUS **MEALS**!

PERISHING **PROVOLONE!** UNCLE TRAP REALLY IS A HUGE GLUTTON!

WE HAVE TO FIND HIM BEFORE HE MAKES MORE TROUBLE!

WELL, WE JUST NEED TO FOLLOW THE TRAIL OF CHAOS...

...THERE'S TRAP!

GOOD AFTERNOON, I'M MR. STILTON. I'M HERE TO REVIEW YOUR DISHES FOR THE RODENT'S GAZETTE...

REALLY...

TRAP!

GERONIMO, CAN'T YOU SEE I'M WORKING?

WHAT WORK? WHAT ARE YOU DOING?

I THOUGHT I'D HELP YOU WITH YOUR **INTERVIEWS**...

EXCUSE US FOR A MOMENT...

I DIDN'T ASK YOU TO HELP ME...

I KNOW, YOU NEVER WANT TO BE HELPED, SO I THOUGHT I'D TAKE THE INITIATIVE...

BZZZZZ

10

SINCE WHEN DID CHEESE START **BUZZING?**

DON'T CHANGE THE SUBJECT! YOU'RE GETTING THE RODENT'S GAZETTE IN TROUBLE!

IT MUST BE ONE OF THOSE GENETICALLY MODIFIED CHEESES...

BZZZ BZZZ

ARE YOU LISTENING TO ME?

MAYBE I'LL HAVE A TASTE...

BZ BZ

STOP, TRAP!

THE CHEESE SPOKE TO ME!

AND GIVEN HOW MUCH CHEESE YOU'VE EATEN, YOU'RE MORE CHEESE THAN A MOUSE BY NOW!

GERONIMO, YOU COME CLOSE, TOO!

COUSIN, IT SEEMS LIKE THE CHEESE KNOWS YOU, TOO!

A TALKING PIECE OF CHEESE? MAYBE WE SHOULD CALL SOMEONE...

WHAT CHEESE? IT IS I, PROFESSOR VON VOLT!

PROFESSOR, WHAT ARE YOU DOING HIDING IN A PIECE OF CHEESE?

UNCLE, I DON'T THINK IT'S....

I'M NOT *INSIDE* THE CHEESE!

THIS IS JUST A SPEAKER! I'M IN MY SUPER-SECRET LAB! I NEED YOU!

WHAT HAPPENED? IS THERE A PROBLEM?

YES, THE TEMPOGRAPH, WHICH I USE TO MAKE SURE HISTORY IS NOT GETTING CHANGED, BEGAN **VIBRATING!**

THE PIRATE CATS?

I BELIEVE SO! THAT'S WHY I NEED TO YOU TO JOIN ME ASAP!

OKAY, BUT HOW CAN WE DO THAT?

YOU REALLY DON'T LIKE TO MAKE THINGS EASY, PROFESSOR!

SCIENCE WOULDN'T BE ANYTHING WITHOUT A TOUCH OF FANTASY... UH, TRAP?

YES?

THERE'S NO POINT INSPECTING IT. THE CHEESE IS *PLASTIC.*

OH.

I'VE PLACED AN ENTRANCE TO MY LABORATORY IN THE POT ON THE LEFT. YOU JUST HAVE TO GET INTO IT AND A PNEUMATIC TUBE WILL BRING YOU TO ME.

GOOD! IF YOU NEED US, PROFESSOR, LET'S NOT KEEP YOU WAITING!

TRAP!

GERONIMOOO!

SPLASH!

WHAT HAVE YOU DONE! MY WONDERFUL CHEESE SOUP!

PROFESSOR, YOUR LAB LOOKS AN AWFUL LOT LIKE A CULINARY STAND...

THE POT ON THE LEFT! VON VOLT SAID THE POT ON THE LEFT!

I FOLLOWED THE SMELL...

WHAT HAVE YOU DONE?!

QUICK, THE SITUATION IS COMING TO A BOIL!

BENJAMIN, THEA, AND BUGSY WUGSY HAVE ALREADY GONE IN. FOLLOW ME SO WE DON'T LOSE ANY MORE TIME.

DON'T WORRY, THAT SOUP WAS NOTHING SPECIAL!

13

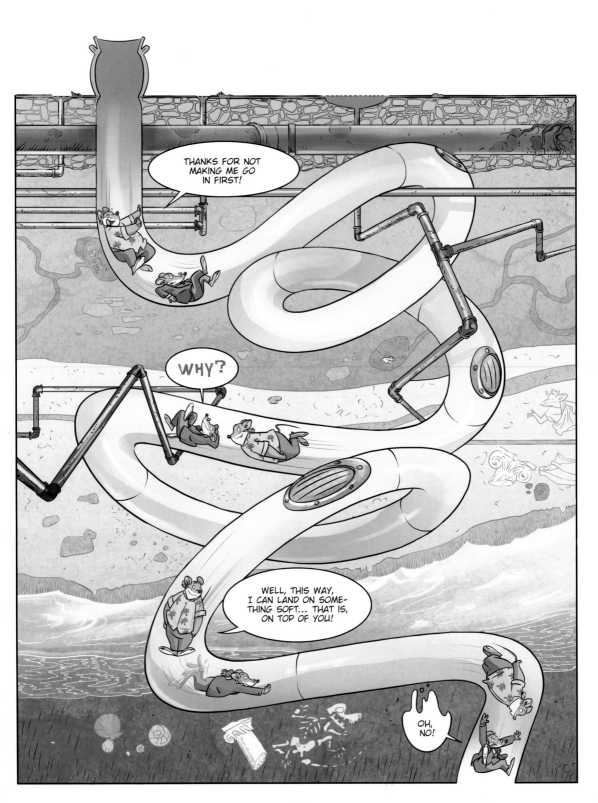

WHY DO YOU SMELL LIKE CHEESE SOUP?

LET'S FORGET ABOUT THAT, PROFESSOR VON VOLT! THE OTHERS HAVE ARRIVED?

THEY'RE WAITING FOR US BY THE TEMPOGRAPH. HURRY! THERE'S NO **TIME** TO LOSE.

I OBSERVED A CHANGE IN THE TEMPORAL FLUX. THE PIRATE CATS ARE TRAVELING INTO THE PAST!

IT'S ALWAYS THEM!

DON'T THEY EVER REST?

BUT WHERE ARE THEY HEADED?

JAPAN IS A COUNTRY THAT LIES OFF THE COAST OF EASTERN ASIA. IT'S MADE UP OF MANY ISLANDS, FOUR MAJOR ONES AND ROUGHLY THREE THOUSAND ITSY-BITSY ONES! 75% OF THE COUNTRY IS MOUNTAINOUS, LARGELY OF VOLCANIC ORIGINS. THE LARGEST PLAIN, KANTO, IS THE SITE OF THE CAPITAL, TOKYO.

ACCORDING TO MY CALCULATIONS, THEY'RE IN JAPAN IN 1603.

THEIR REASON FOR BEING THERE, HOWEVER, ESCAPES ME!

MAYBE THEY MADE A MISTAKE!

THE PIRATE CATS AREN'T VERY PRECISE, IT'S TRUE, BUT THEY SELDOM MAKE A MISTAKE IN THE DESTINATION FOR THEIR TRIPS. THIS IS WHY I NEED YOU TO GO TO JAPAN AND *INVESTIGATE* COME, YOUR COSTUMES ARE IN THE SPEEDRAT!

I'VE ALREADY BEEN TO JAPAN! THIS TIME I'LL BE ABLE TO DRESS LIKE A SAMURAI?

YOU, A SAMURAI? SINCE WHEN DID YOU GET SO BRAVE?

ACTUALLY... I THOUGHT OF SOMETHING SIMPLER. GERONIMO, TRAP, AND BENJAMIN WILL BE STREET PERFORMERS, ACCOMPANIED BY THEA AND BUGSY WUGSY.

SAMURAI WERE VERY FAMOUS WARRIORS WITH NOBLE ORIGINS IN THE FEUDAL ERA. THEY WERE ESPECIALLY SKILLED IN THE USE OF THE SWORD AND HAD TWO SABERS AS THEIR EMBLEM, A SHORT ONE (WAKIZASHI) AND A LONGER ONE (KATANA). THEY FOLLOWED A VERY RIGID CODE OF HONOR.

VERY GOOD. THE COSTUMES ARE ALL HERE AND ALSO THE EQUIPMENT THAT WILL LET YOU UNDERSTAND THE LANGUAGE OF THE TIME. NOW, HURRY UP! YOU HAVE TO PREVENT THE CATS FROM CHANGING THE PAST!

DON'T WORRY, PROFESSOR, WE'LL SEE TO IT!

WHERE EXACTLY ARE WE HEADED?

YOU'LL ARRIVE A LITTLE BIT AWAY FROM EDO, THE ANCIENT NAME FOR TOKYO. HIDE THE SPEEDRAT AND DISGUISE YOURSELVES WITHOUT ANYONE DISCOVERING YOU!

TOKYO HAS BEEN THE CAPITAL OF JAPAN SINCE 1868, WHEN THE EMPEROR DECIDED TO MOVE THE SEAT OF THE GOVERNMENT AND HIS OWN RESIDENCE THERE. UNTIL THEN, IT HAD BEEN CALLED EDO, FROM THE NAME OF THE CASTLE (NAMED EDO-JO, BUILT IN 1457) THAT DOMINATED THE AREA.

THE PREPARATIONS WERE ALL MADE. ALL THAT WAS LEFT WAS TO BEGIN THE MISSION...

VRRRRRR

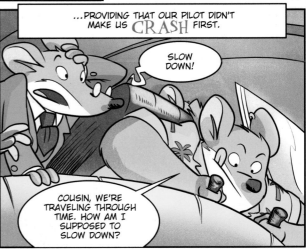

...PROVIDING THAT OUR PILOT DIDN'T MAKE US **CRASH** FIRST.

SLOW DOWN!

COUSIN, WE'RE TRAVELING THROUGH TIME. HOW AM I SUPPOSED TO SLOW DOWN?

IN THE MEANTIME, CATARDONE III, EMPEROR OF THE PIRATE CATS, HIS DAUGHTER TERSILLA, AND THEIR ASSISTANT, BONZO, HAD ARRIVED IN JAPAN, IN 1603. THEY'D MADE MISTAKES, HOWEVER, IN A FEW OF THEIR CALCULATIONS...

MOUNT FUJI MT. FUJI IS A VOLCANO AND THE TALLEST MOUNTAIN IN JAPAN (3,776 METERS). ITS SNOWY PEAK IS ONE OF THE MOST FAMOUS SYMBOLS OF THE COUNTRY. THE JAPANESE CONSIDER IT HOLY AND MAKE A PILGRIMAGE TO ITS SLOPES AT LEAST ONCE DURING THEIR LIVES.

WHAT ARE WE DOING NEAR MT. FUJI?

YOU TOLD ME WE HAD TO GO TO JAPAN, AND THIS IS JAPAN, RIGHT?

MT. FUJI'S FAR FROM EDO. HOW DO YOU THINK WE'RE GOING TO GET THERE?

UMM...

WE'LL FIND A WAY TO GET AROUND AND WE'RE NOT IN A HURRY. NO ONE KNOWS WE'RE HERE AND OUR MOUSE MASKS ARE STILL WORKING!

I STILL DON'T GET WHAT WE'RE DOING IN JAPAN IN 1603... IT'S COUNTRY-SIDE ALL AROUND HERE!

YOU'RE ALWAYS MOUSING OFF,* AND THAT'S WHY YOU'LL ALWAYS BE AN ASSISTANT, WHILE MY FATHER IS EMPEROR OF THE PIRATE CATS!

*TALKING NONSENSE!

I'M FINALLY GOING TO MEET ONE OF MY PEERS, THE HEAD OF JAPAN! FINALLY, SOMEONE WHO WILL UNDERSTAND THE WEIGHT OF POWER!

YOU MEAN HE'S FAT LIKE YOU?

HOW DARE YOU ADDRESS YOUR EMPEROR THAT WAY?! BEG FOR MY PARDON IMMEDIATELY!

FORGIVE ME, FORGIVE ME, OH, SUPREME EMPEROR!

LET'S GO, WITHOUT LOSING ANY MORE TIME! EDO'S STILL FAR AWAY.

WAIT FOR US: YOU'VE GOT THE MAP!

IN THE MEANTIME, WE'D ARRIVED NEAR EDO, HIDDEN THE SPEEDRAT AND PUT ON OUR COSTUMES.

ANCIENT ARCHITECTURE
IN OLD JAPAN, THE SIMPLEST BUILDINGS WERE BUILT OUT OF INEXPENSIVE MATERIALS LIKE WOOD AND STRAW, AS THE COUNTRY WAS FULL OF FORESTS. MORE IMPORTANT BUILDINGS WERE BUILT OUT OF MORE DURABLE MATERIALS, SUCH AS STONE.

YUM! IT SEEMS RIGHT THAT WE ARRIVED IN TIME FOR DINNER!

OUCH!

HOW MANY TIMES HAVE I TOLD YOU NOT TO BUILD A FIRE CLOSE TO THE HUTS, HAYAO? ALL IT TAKES IS ONE SPARK AND EVERYTHING'LL GO UP IN FLAMES!

GRANDPA! WHAT'D I DO WRONG THIS TIME?

DO FIRES HAPPEN OFTEN AROUND HERE?

OH, WHEN TOKUGAWA CAME THINGS GOT BETTER. HE BARRED CONSTRUCTION OF NEW BUILDINGS WITH STRAW ROOFS, WHICH PREVENTED THE DESTRUCTION OF ENTIRE DISTRICTS IN A SINGLE BLAZE, EVEN THOUGH...

EVEN THOUGH...?

RECENTLY, THE FIRES HAVE RESUMED, BUT THIS TIME THEY'RE ALSO HAPPENING IN BUILDINGS MADE OF STONE. THEY SAY IT'S...

FOOLS, AND MY NEPHEW, SAY THAT THE GHOST OF THE OLD COMMANDER IS BEHIND THESE FIRES, THAT HE CAN'T FIND PEACE AFTER THE DEFEAT AT SEKIGAHARA.

THE BATTLE OF SEKIGAHARA IN 1600 CONFIRMED THE POWER OF GENERAL TOKUGAWA IEYASU, WHO WAS NAMED "SHOGUN" (IN OTHER WORDS, GRAND GENERAL) OF THE EMPEROR GO-YOZEI IN 1603, AT THE AGE OF 60. AFTERWARDS, HE ESTABLISHED EDO (THE FUTURE TOKYO) AS THE SEAT OF THE BAKUFU (THE GOVERNMENT OF THE SHOGUNATE), WHICH IN VERY LITTLE TIME BECAME THE BIGGEST CITY IN JAPAN.

YOU'RE NOT FROM AROUND HERE. WHO ARE YOU?

MY NAME IS GERO-NIMURA STIL-TAO AND THIS IS MY COUSIN TRAPOSHIRO. WE'RE ACTORS AND WE'VE COME TO EDO TO LOOK FOR WORK.

ACTORS THAT'S FANTASTIC! WELCOME, FRIENDS! I'LL GET THE FIRE READY FOR DINNER.

DINNER PROCEEDED CALMLY. WE HAD A MISSION TO CARRY OUT, BUT WE CERTAINLY COULDN'T REFUSE SUCH A WARM WELCOME!

UNTIL...

SINCE YOU'RE HERE, WHY DON'T YOU PERFORM NOW? SOMETHING SIMPLE, JUST TO LET US SEE HOW GOOD YOU ARE!

WHA... ->COUGH<-... ->COUGH<-...

YES, DEFINITELY! WE KNOW THE TASTES OF THE COURT VERY WELL! WE CAN TELL YOU IF YOU'LL BE SUCCESSFUL!

TRAPPOSHIRO AND I REALLY SHOULD HAVE A LITTLE REHEARSAL FIRST...

I'LL GO RIGHT NOW AND GET AN OLD SAMURAI SUIT OF ARMOR, SO YOU CAN USE IT FOR THE PERFORMANCE!

UNCLE, ARE YOU SURE YOU WANT TO DO THIS?

I'M A SCAREDY MOUSE, BUT WHAT ALTERNATIVE DO WE HAVE?

NO! NO! NO! NO!

MAYBE THEY DON'T WANT GERONIMO TO SING?

NO, DEAR, THEY'RE TALKING ABOUT NOH THEATER.

NOH THEATER
NOH DRAMA WAS A TYPE OF THEATER POPULAR IN 14TH CENTURY JAPAN, WHICH RETOLD STORIES OF HEROIC EVENTS FROM JAPANESE TRADITION THROUGH SONG, ACTING, AND DANCE. THE ACTORS WERE ALL MEN, EVEN IN WOMEN'S ROLES, AND THEY WORE DISTINCTIVE MASKS.

ALLOW ME TO PERFORM A DANCE BEFORE MY BROTHERS BEGIN THEIR PLAY...

?

?!?

A WOMAN WHO ACTS? WHAT KIND OF STRANGENESS IS THIS?

23

ONLY MEN PERFORM IN NOH THEATER!

AH!

?!

!!!

THESE ORANGES WILL BE BETTER IN MY BELLY, AFTER THE PLAY...

FOK

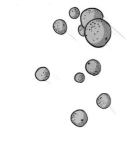

!! !! !! !!

LOOK OUT, UNCLE!

PLONK
PLONK
PLONK
PLONK
PLONK
PLONK
PLONK
PLONK

?!

OHHHH!

...ON THE FLY...

HE SPEARED THEM...

...WITH A WOODEN **SWORD!**

THAT'S WHY HE DIDN'T WANT TO PERFORM... GERO-NIMU-RA STIL-TAO IS A RONIN WHO'S PRETENDING TO BE AN ACTOR!

RONIN
RONIN WERE SAMURAI WHO DIDN'T SERVE A SINGLE LORD, BUT RATHER WANDERING WARRIORS AVAILABLE TO WORK FOR PAY.

WONDERFUL, UNCLE!

YOU WERE INCREDIBLE!

THEY CAN STILL BE EATEN, RIGHT?

LATER THAT NIGHT...

FIRE! FIRE!

WHAT'S GOING ON?

ONE OF THE HOUSES IS GOING UP IN FLAMES! WE NEED TO HELP WITH THE BUCKETS!

HOW CAN WE HELP?

ZZZZ

GO UP IN THE WATCHTOWER AND SHOW US THE FLASHPOINT.

WAKE UP, TRAP. THERE'S NO TIME TO LOSE.

ZZ-- MHM. LET ME SLEEP...

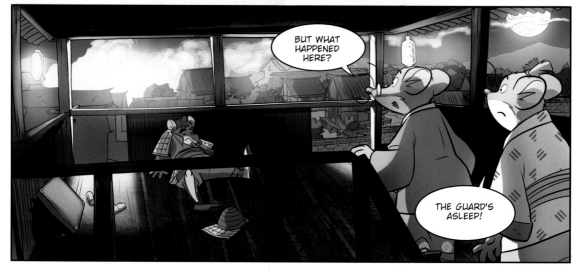

BUT WHAT HAPPENED HERE?

THE GUARD'S ASLEEP!

HE'S MORE THAN ASLEEP. IT SEEMS LIKE SOMEONE PUT HIM OUT OF ACTION. THIS IS NOT THE WORK OF A GHOST...

THE FIRE'S THREE STREETS DOWN, ON THE LEFT!

OKAY!

?!

TAP TAP

?!

OUR "GHOST" IS ON THE ROOF. WE'VE GOT TO CATCH UP WITH HIM!

I'LL HELP YOU CLIMB UP!

MOLDY MOZZARELLA! WE'RE HIGH UP!

∻PANT!∻

∻PANT!∻

STOP!

?!

ALMOST THERE.

GOT 'IM!

RRRIPP

NO!

BY A WHISKER...

NOW WE KNOW IT'S NOT A GHOST CAUSING THESE FIRES AND WE'VE GOT A CLUE...

IN THE MEANTIME, MY FAME AS AN ACTOR HAD SPREAD TO THE FOUR WINDS AND I HAD BEEN INVITED TO COURT.

WHAT'RE ALL THESE COMINGS AND GOINGS?

THE EDO-JO CASTLE ISN'T YET FINISHED. THE WING FOR SHOGUN TOKUGAWA IEYASU IS READY, BUT THERE'S STILL MUCH TO DO.

SO WHY DOES THE EMPEROR WANT TO SEE US?

NO, NO, TOKUGAWA IEYASU ISN'T THE EMPEROR. HE'S THE SHOGUN! THAT'S A VERY POWERFUL FAMILY WHO GOVERNS THIS REGION.

SHOGUN
THE TITLE THAT IN ANCIENT JAPAN WAS GIVEN TO THE HEAD OF MILITARY EXPEDITIONS. STARTING IN 1192, THE TITLE BECAME HEREDITARY AND SHOGUN BECAME THE DE FACTO RULERS OF THE COUNTRY, WHILE THE ROLE OF EMPEROR MAINLY RETAINED A HISTORICAL FUNCTION.

THE PAST FEW DAYS, THE SHOGUN HAS BEEN DECIDING HOW TO DIVIDE THE FIEFDOMS AMONG HIS MOST FAITHFUL SUBJECTS.

WE'VE FINALLY DISCOVERED WHY THE PIRATE CATS HAVE COME TO THIS PERIOD: TO GET A FIEFDOM TO PASS DOWN TO THEIR OWN DESCENDANTS!

BUT WHY ARE THEY LIGHTING THE FIRES? WHAT DO THEY GAIN FROM DESTROYING THE CITY?

RELAX! I'M HERE TO PROTECT YOU, TRAP THE CAT-NABBER!

That's the shogun. Go to the guards to speak with him. You're expected!

Ahem... Hello, I am Gero-Nimura Stil-Tao, shogun Ieyasu wanted to see me...

Stil-Tao! Finally! I've heard much talk about you! They say you were able to spear 10 oranges without looking!

Well, actually...

And if you did this for the peasants, I imagine that at this evening's CELEBRATION, you'll do even better!

I don't know if...

Don't contradict him. It could be DANGEROUS!

This evening, I'll assign strongholds to my most faithful representatives and you will perform a play worthy of my court!

Uh, oh, things aren't looking so good here...

HURRAH!

IT'LL BE AN UNFORGETTABLE EVENING!

WHAT'S GOING ON?

STILTON AND HIS FRIENDS HAVE COME TO SWIPE THE HERRING FROM OUR BARREL!

HAVE THEY IDENTIFIED US?

THAT SUFFERING SQUEAKER! ALWAYS STICKING HIS **PAWS** INTO EVERYTHING!

NO, BONZO ASSURED ME THEY DIDN'T RECOGNIZE US YESTERDAY EVENING. BUT WE HAVE TO ACT WITH GREAT CAUTION AND TIME IS PRESSING!

WHEN WE MAKE THE SHOGUN OUR OFFER, HE'LL GIVE US ALL WE ASK FOR!

WHY DO I ALWAYS HAVE TO DO THE HARD WORK?

WE HAVE TO GIVE THE SHOGUN ALL OUR SUPPORT IF WE'RE GOING TO CONVINCE HIM WE'RE HIS ALLIES AND DESERVE HIS HELP!

EVEN THOUGH WE'VE ARRIVED AFTER THE BATTLE OF SEKIGAHARA, WE STILL HAVE A GOOD CHANCE OF GETTING THE FIEFDOM WE WANT AND BECOMING TOZAMA DAIMYO!

AND WHAT'S THAT!

DIVIDING THE TERRITORY
AFTER THE VICTORY OF SEKIGAHARA, SHOGUN TOKUGAWA IEYASU AWARDED NEW LANDS TO THE VASSALS WHO HAD SERVED HIM. THE FUDAI DAIMYO WERE HIS ALLIES AT THE TIME, AND THOSE WHO SUBMITTED TO HIS AUTHORITY AFTER THE BATTLE CAME TO BE KNOWN AS THE TOZAMA DAIMYO.

BON-ZAI, DON'T SLACK OFF! BE QUICK WITH THAT SACK!

YES, OKAY!

THIS TIME GERONIMO AND HIS FAMILY CAN TRY EVERY WAY THEY WISH BUT THEY WON'T BE ABLE TO STOP US!

HEE HEE HEE!

HMM...

MAYBE THAT'S THE WAY TO THE **KITCHEN**...

TRAP, WE'RE IN TROUBLE!

GERONIMO HAS TO PERFORM TONIGHT AND WE DON'T EVEN KNOW WHERE THE PIRATE CATS ARE!

THEA, YOU STAY WITH THE KIDS AND TRY TO COME UP WITH AN IDEA FOR MY PERFORMANCE THIS EVENING. WE NEED SOMETHING SPECIAL...

GERONIMO AND I WILL DEAL WITH THE INVESTIGATION...

...MY NOSE FOR INVESTIGATING IS SECOND ONLY TO MY NOSE FOR CHEESE!

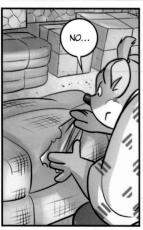

NO...

NO...

NO...

NO...

NO...

HOW DARE YOU!

IT'S NOT EVEN HIM...

TRAP, YOU CAN'T ACT THIS WAY! THESE ARE GOVERNMENT DIGNITARIES, WHILE WE ARE SIMPLE ARTISTS!

WE'RE SO SORRY!

JAPANESE SOCIETY
IN THE EDO PERIOD, JAPANESE SOCIETY HAD A VERY RIGID STRUCTURE AND WAS DIVIDED INTO FOUR CASTES. THE MOST IMPORTANT WAS THE MILITARY (THE SHOGUN AND THE SAMURAI), FOLLOWED BY PEASANTS, ARTISANS, AND MERCHANTS. THE CASTE SYSTEM WAS ABOLISHED IN 1871.

IF WE WANT TO CARRY OUT OUR INVESTIGATION, WE HAVE TO BE MORE DISCREET.

BUT ALL WE HAVE TO DO IS FIND WHO HAS A TUNIC WITH THIS PATTERN AND WE'LL FIND OUT WHO SET THE FIRE!

ANOTHER WAY TO INVESTIGATE IS TO FIGURE OUT WHAT MIGHT BE ATTRACTING THE PIRATE CATS-- WHICH FIEFDOM THEY'RE LOOKING AT.

ASK THAT RODENT FOR INFORMATION.

DID YOU WANT TO ASK ME SOMETHING?

UH...

DO YOU KNOW WHERE THE KITCHEN IS?

HE'S INCORRIGIBLE...

AS I RECALL, THE KITCHEN SHOULD BE THIS WAY...

EXCUSE ME, COUSIN!

SINCE TRAP HAD BEEN DRAWN TO THE KITCHEN, IT WAS LEFT TO ME TO FIND A TRUSTWORTHY PERSON THAT I COULD ASK FOR INFORMATION...

...IN ORDER TO GET TO THE BOTTOM OF THIS MYSTERY!

-AHEM!- EXCUSE ME...

GERO-NIMURA STIL-TAO! I JUST FINISHED MY SHIFT. IF YOU WANT TO SPEAK WITH THE *SHOGUN*, HE'S IN THE HALL.

NO, NO...

...I JUST WANTED TO TALK TO YOU ABOUT THE PERFORMANCE!

I'M JUST A GUARD. HOW CAN I HELP YOU?

I KNOW THAT THE FIEFDOMS WILL BE AWARDED THIS EVENING, BUT I WANTED TO GET SOME INFORMATION, SO WE COULD MAKE OUR PERFORMANCE FIT THE OCCASION.

THE PLAY'S ALMOST READY NOW...

SEKIGAHARA, OCTOBER 21, 1600.

AFTER THE BATTLE THAT DECIDED TOKUGAWA IEYASU'S VICTORY, WE ALL KNEW THAT WE WERE HEADED TOWARDS A NEW ERA FOR JAPAN...

...SO NO ONE LOST ANY TIME: EVERYONE RUSHED TO TOKUGAWA IEYASU TO SWEAR ALLEGIANCE TO HIM.

THE TOZAMA DAIMYO, HOWEVER, HAD TO PROVE THEIR ALLEGIANCE TO THE SHOGUN, SINCE THEY HADN'T FOUGHT FOR HIM.

THE FUDAI DAIMYO, WHO WERE ALREADY VASSALS OF TOKUGAWA, WEREN'T GOING TO HAVE ANY PROBLEM GETTING THE TERRITORIES THEY DESERVED.

TOKUGAWA HAS BEEN VERY PRUDENT WITH THEM, WHICH IS WHY, FOR THE PAST THREE YEARS, HE'S STILL BEEN CHOOSING WHO HE'LL AWARD THE LAST FIEFDOMS TO.

AND AMONG THESE LORDS, IS THERE ONE WHO ARRIVED AT THE LAST MINUTE? OR WHO'S ACTING **STRANGELY?**

FOR SURE. I CAN'T SAY THAT THE MEOWZAKI FAMILY HAS BEEN SCHOOLED WELL IN PROPER BEHAVIOR... BUT, ON THE OTHER HAND, THEY'RE ASKING FOR A FIEFDOM THAT NO ONE ELSE WANTS!

HOW COME?

WELL, IT'S ONE OF THE PROVINCES NEAREST EDO CASTLE AND TOO MUCH UNDER THE INFLUENCE OF THE SHOGUN.

I'M GOING NOW. SEE YOU AFTER THE **PERFORMANCE!**

UHM... YES.

UNCLE, YOU HAVE TO GET READY!

WE MANAGED TO FIND TWO OF THE OLD COURT COMPANY'S **COSTUMES.** BUT YOU AND TRAP AT LEAST HAVE TO MAKE AN ATTEMPT NOW...

IN THE MEANTIME, ANY NEWS?

I THINK THE PIRATE CATS ARE HIDING BEHIND THE MEOWZAKI FAMILY. THEY'RE THE LAST ONES WHO GOT HERE TO ASK FOR A FIEFDOM.

BUT IF WE KNOW WHO THEY ARE, WHY DON'T WE UNMASK THEM?

WE DON'T HAVE ANY **PROOF** AND THE SHOGUN FAVORS THEM...

A LITTLE LATER, THAT EVENING...

IEYASU-SAMA, IF I MIGHT SAY A WORD BEFORE THE BEGINNING OF THE CEREMONY...

WE'LL ONLY TAKE A MOMENT AND WON'T DISTURB YOU MORE!

CATORO MEOWZAKI, WHAT OTHER **STRANGE** PROPOSAL DO YOU HAVE FOR ME?

THE BUILD OF THAT RODENT LOOKS FAMILIAR TO ME...

I HAVE THE PLANS WITH ME FOR A **CART** THAT CAN CARRY PEOPLE AND THINGS WITHOUT USING HORSES OR MULES!

INTERESTING! HOW DOES IT WORK?

WE'RE DEVELOPING THE LAST TECHNICAL DETAILS, BUT IF YOU'LL GRANT MY REQUEST...

YOU PERSIST IN YOUR DESIRE FOR THE FIEFDOM NEXT TO THE CASTLE, EVEN THOUGH IT'S SO SMALL.

TO BE NEAR YOU, MY SHOGUN, IS VERY IMPORTANT!

I GET IT! THE CATS WANT TO GET THEIR HANDS ON THE DISTRICT THAT'S CALLED *MINATO KU* TODAY. IT'S THE CENTER OF THE JAPANESE AUTOMOBILE MANUFACTURING BUSINESS. THEY WILL BECOME VERY RICH!

I STILL HAVE TO THINK ABOUT IT...

AND TO CONCLUDE...

CLAP CLAP

TO SHOW THE MEOWZAKI FAMILY'S DEDICATION, WE CARRIED OUT OUR OWN INVESTIGATIONS INTO THE RECENT FREQUENT FIRES AND FOUND THE CULPRIT!

?!

?!

?!

?!

?!

HAYAO? BUT WHAT IS HE DOING HERE?

THE SITUATION'S GETTING COMPLICATED...

WE FOUND HIM THIS AFTERNOON IN THE VICINITY OF THE **CASTLE**, AND WE KNOW HE'S DARED TO START FIRES NEAR HIS HOUSE MANY TIMES.

I'M INNOCENT. I DIDN'T DO ANYTHING!

BUT THEY CAN'T ACCUSE HIM WITHOUT PROOF!

HAYAO IS A LEATHER TANNER. THE WORD OF TWO DIGNITARIES IS ENOUGH TO CHARGE HIM, UNFORTUNATELY.

AS YOU SEE, MY SHOGUN, WE HAVEN'T JUST FOILED A DIRECT THREAT TO EDO CASTLE, BUT, IF YOU AWARD THIS FIEFDOM TO THE MEOWZAKI FAMILY, THERE WILL BE NO MORE FIRES!

HMM...

YOU! WHAT DO YOU HAVE TO SAY IN YOUR DEFENSE?

I ADMIT I'M AN ABSENT-MINDED RAT, BUT I'M NOT AN ARSONIST!

JUST YESTERDAY, I PUT OUT ONE OF THE *FIRES* THAT HAD FLARED UP!

WE CAN TESTIFY TO THAT. HE WOKE US UP IMMEDIATELY!

→GULP.←

AND WHO'S TO SAY HE DIDN'T WAKE YOU UP AFTER STARTING THE FIRE?

OR THAT YOU AREN'T HIS ACCOMPLICES?

THIS IS GOING TO GO BADLY IF WE DON'T DO SOMETHING....

BUT WE HAVE PROOF!

WE RIPPED THIS SCRAP OF FABRIC WHEN WE WERE CHASING HIM ON THE WATCHTOWER. HE DIDN'T REALIZE IT, AND WE CAN **IDENTIFY** HIM!

-:GULP!:-

SO WE CAN EASILY SHOW WHO THE CULPRIT IS!

COUSIN!

TRAP, DON'T YOU SEE THAT WE'RE DISCUSSING SOMETHING IMPORTANT HERE?

YES, I KNOW, BUT YOU KNOW... I SPENT SO MUCH TIME INVESTIGATING... I WANT TO SAY WHO THE CULPRIT IS!

ARE YOU SURE YOU'VE FIGURED OUT WHO THE CULPRIT IS?

OF COURSE, I ALREADY KNEW BEFORE, BUT I WAS WAITING FOR THE RIGHT MOMENT!

SO GO AHEAD THEN!

SO? ARE YOU GOING TO TELL ME WHO THE CULPRIT IS, IN YOUR OPINION?

IEYASU-SAMA, MEMBERS OF THE COURT OF *EDO*...

AFTER CAREFUL INVESTIGATION AND HOURS OF EXTENSIVE INQUIRIES, THE TRUE CULPRIT GAVE HIMSELF AWAY BEFORE MY VERY EYES. I WAITED UNTIL THE LAST MOMENT TO BE SURE, BUT NOW I CAN TELL YOU THAT THE CULPRIT IS--

THE CULPRIT IS--

THE DIGNITARY HOKUZWA!

AND THERE'S ONLY ONE WAY TO PROVE IT!

OHHHH!

I NEED TO TEAR OFF HIS MASK!

AHHHH! HELP!

YOUR **MASKS** ARE REALLY STURDY, YOU CRUMMY CATS!

STOP!

GET HIM OFF ME!

HE'S THE CULPRIT!

ORDER! ORDER!

BUT WHAT'S HE DOING?

HE ATTACKED THE DIGNITARY HOKUZAWA!

I ONLY ARRIVED IN EDO THIS MORNING. HOW AM I SUPPOSED TO HAVE SET A FIRE YESTERDAY EVENING?

REALLY?

WELL... THEN MAYBE... I COULD BE **MISTAKEN...**

?!

STOP!

THE CULPRIT IS THIS FAKE SAMURAI! LOOK: THE *FABRIC* WE FOUND IS THE SAME AS WHAT HE'S WEARING!

IT'S A DRESS LIKE MANY OTHERS; IT COULD BE ANYBODY'S!

CALL THE WATCHTOWER GUARD TO TESTIFY THEN!

HE DIDN'T SEE ME WHEN I HIT HIM OVER THE **HEAD!**

OOPS.

BONZO, WHEN WE GET HOME, I'M GOING TO THROW YOU INTO THE SEA...

STOP, EVERYONE! IF ANYONE TAKES A STEP, I'LL TRIM HIS SAILS*!

AHHH!

IF YOU WANT YOUR SHOGUN IN ONE PIECE, THROW DOWN YOUR **ARMS!**

CLUNK

CLUNK

MOLDY MOZZARELLA, CATARDONE! IT'S TOO LATE! YOU'RE NOT GOING TO GET A FIEFDOM!

THEN I'LL BE SATISFIED WITH BECOMING THE EMPEROR OF JAPAN! AND THE RULES APPLY TO YOU, TOO, YOU LOUSY RAT! THROW DOWN YOUR SWORD!

*CRUSH HIM!

CLUNK

CLUNK

?!

CLUNK

CLUNK

SO I WILL BE THE EMPEROR OF THE CATS AND OF JAPAN AT LAST!

CLUNK

CLUNK

CLUNK

CLUNK !

GMMMNG-

BUT WHAT--

GMMMNG-

IN THE END, WE DIDN'T HAVE TO CREATE AN ARTISTIC ACT AT ALL: THE SHOGUN SAID THAT WE'D ALREADY DONE ENOUGH FOR THAT EVENING AND SHOULD JUST THINK ABOUT ENJOYING OURSELVES!

BUT A FEW ACTORS INVITED THEA TO PARTICIPATE IN A TYPE OF **PLAY** THAT HAD RECENTLY BEGUN IN JAPAN, KABUKI!

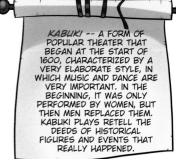

KABUKI -- A FORM OF POPULAR THEATER THAT BEGAN AT THE START OF 1600, CHARACTERIZED BY A VERY ELABORATE STYLE, IN WHICH MUSIC AND DANCE ARE VERY IMPORTANT. IN THE BEGINNING, IT WAS ONLY PERFORMED BY WOMEN, BUT THEN MEN REPLACED THEM. KABUKI PLAYS RETELL THE DEEDS OF HISTORICAL FIGURES AND EVENTS THAT REALLY HAPPENED.

WHEN IT WAS TIME FOR US TO GO, WE WERE VERY SAD TO LEAVE SUCH A NICE CELEBRATION, BUT WE WERE HAPPY TO HAVE SAVED THE HISTORY OF JAPAN!

BUT WE'D MADE PROFESSOR WAIT TOO LONG, AND HE WAS UNDOUBTEDLY WORRIED.

Watch Out For PAPERCUTZ

Welcome to the time-tripping twelfth GERONIMO STILTON graphic novel from Papercutz, the cheese-loving folks dedicated to publishing great graphic novels for all ages. I'm Salicrup, *Jim Salicrup*, the Editor-in-Chief around here, happy that my job isn't even half as dangerous as being editor of The Rodent's Gazette!

Wow! I was thrilled just to know that this GERONIMO STILTON graphic novel would be taking place in Japan in 1603, but when I discovered that Thea Stilton was back, as well— I simply can't tell you how excited I was! **MOLDY MOZZARELLA!** THEA STILTON #1 "The Secret of Whale Island" is coming soon, and fans couldn't be any happier! While Thea actually does appear in the series, the real stars are the Thea Sisters, five students at Mouseford College, who want to become journalists like their hero, Thea Stilton! If you love Thea Stilton you'll want fo pick up THEA STILTON #1 "The Secret of Whale Island"! Everyone's talking about how Thea may now become the real super-star in the Stilton family! Even if she sort of made a big boo-boo when she tried to perform…

The above scene is a great example of how much the world has changed! It's hard to believe that there was a time when women weren't allowed to become actors, and now, through the wonder of time travel, that same woman is such a successful journalist that she's inspiring a whole new generation of girls to follow in her footsteps.

But why should the Stiltons have all the fun? How would you like to take a short, quick trip through time? Simply turn the page and you'll see actual pages from the very next GERONIMO STILTON graphic novel in your future: "The Fastest Train in the West"! Ironically, your peek into the future is set in the Old West! That's what we love to call a Time Paradox, something that doesn't really make any sense. Something that should be impossible, yet there it is!

See you in the future!

STAY IN TOUCH!

EMAIL: salicrup@papercutz.com
WEB: www.papercutz.com
TWITTER: @papercutzgn
FACEBOOK: PAPERCUTZGRAPHICNOVELS
FAN MAIL: Papercutz, 160 Broadway, Suite 700, East Wing, New York, NY 10038

Caricature of Jim by Steve Brodner at the MoCCA Art Fest.

AND BESIDES, I'M VERY GLAD TO AVOID ANOTHER FLIGHT IN THE SPEEDRAT WITH TRAP! THAT WOULD BE THE THIRD IN A SHORT TIME!

HEE! HEE! HEE!

TRAP, YOU SHOULD TRY TO GET HIRED AS A WORKER AT THE CONSTRUCTION SITE. THEA, TRY TO KEEP OUR COUSIN FROM SLOWING DOWN THE CONSTRUCTION WORK.

HEY!

!!!

REMEMBER, WE DON'T KNOW WHERE OR WHEN THE PIRATE CATS WILL SWING INTO ACTION!

CALM DOWN, COUSIN, WE'LL SEE TO IT!

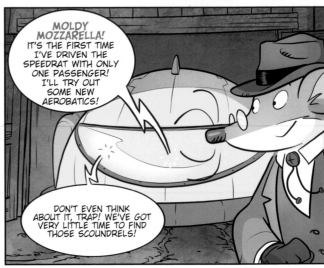

MOLDY MOZZARELLA! IT'S THE FIRST TIME I'VE DRIVEN THE SPEEDRAT WITH ONLY ONE PASSENGER! I'LL TRY OUT SOME NEW AEROBATICS!

DON'T EVEN THINK ABOUT IT, TRAP! WE'VE GOT VERY LITTLE TIME TO FIND THOSE SCOUNDRELS!

COME ON, KIDS, LET'S GO CHECK OUT THE WILD WEST!

THE WILD WEST (FAR WEST OR OLD WEST) WAS A TERM USED IN THE 1800s FOR THE REGION BETWEEN THE GREAT PLAINS AND THE ROCKY MOUNTAINS, EXTENDING WESTWARDS FROM THE MISSISSIPPI RIVER TO THE PACIFIC OCEAN AND TOWARDS CANADA. THE AREA WAS INHABITED BY NATIVE AMERICANS, THAT IS TO SAY, AMERICAN INDIANS.

IN THE MEANTIME, TRAP AND THEA HAD REACHED THE CONSTRUCTION SITE FOR THE RAIL LINE THAT WAS HEADING EASTWARDS.

BUT IF WE LEAVE THE SPEEDRAT HERE, HOW WILL WE GET IT BACK? IT'S IN THE MIDDLE OF THE DESERT!

EASY, WE'LL BRING IT WITH US!

THE WORK SITE MOVES WITH THE WORKERS, SO THE CRATES WON'T REMAIN HERE.

UH, NO?

TO BE OPENED AT THE INAUGURATION.

THEY'LL COME WITH US UNTIL THE WORK IS FINISHED. IT'S ENOUGH TO PROVIDE EXACT INFORMATION. THIS CRATE WILL BE ONE OF THE MANY THAT ARE FOR THE INAUGURATION!

GREAT! NOW ALL THAT'S LEFT IS TO START LOOKING FOR THOSE CRUMMY CATS!

EXCUSE ME, GENTLE-MOUSE!

WHO ME?

MY COUSIN AND I WOULD LIKE TO HELP WITH THE WONDERFUL PROJECT YOU'RE WORKING ON! WHAT CAN WE DO?

WELL, YOU CAN GIVE THE STOKERS A HAND. YOUR COUSIN CAN DEAL WITH THE SUPPLIES. IN THE LAST FEW DAYS THERE'VE BEEN A LOT OF PROBLEMS WITH THE INVENTORY.

WHAT KIND OF PROBLEMS?

THE CRATES SEEM TO HAVE GOTTEN SCRAMBLED. SOMETIMES IT TAKES A WHOLE DAY TO FIND THE PIECES WE NEED.

BETWEEN THESE GLITCHES, THE EXPLOSION IN THE **TUNNEL**, AND THE BAD WEATHER WHEN WE GOT HERE, IT'S NOT FUNNY!

OKAY! WE'LL START LOOKING HERE!

"LOOKING HERE" FOR WHAT?

NO, MY COUSIN MEANT WE'D START LOOKING FOR WORK HERE!

AH!

WE'RE SEEING THE PAW PRINTS OF THE PIRATE CATS HERE!

RIGHT! THEY MUST BE THE ONE WHO'VE CREATED THE CONFUSION WITH THE SUPPLIES.

I WONDER HOW GERONIMO'S FARING?